G000108209

LONELY PLANET'S
WHERE TO GO WHEN

2018

JANUARY
M	T	W	T	F	S	S
1	2	3	4	5	6	7
8	9	10	11	12	13	14
15	16	17	18	19	20	21
22	23	24	25	26	27	28
29	30	31				

FEBRUARY
M	T	W	T	F	S	S
			1	2	3	4
5	6	7	8	9	10	11
12	13	14	15	16	17	18
19	20	21	22	23	24	25
26	27	28				

MARCH
M	T	W	T	F	S	S
			1	2	3	4
5	6	7	8	9	10	11
12	13	14	15	16	17	18
19	20	21	22	23	24	25
26	27	28	29	30	31	

APRIL
M	T	W	T	F	S	S
						1
2	3	4	5	6	7	8
9	10	11	12	13	14	15
16	17	18	19	20	21	22
23	24	25	26	27	28	29
30						

MAY
M	T	W	T	F	S	S
	1	2	3	4	5	6
7	8	9	10	11	12	13
14	15	16	17	18	19	20
21	22	23	24	25	26	27
28	29	30	31			

JUNE
M	T	W	T	F	S	S
				1	2	3
4	5	6	7	8	9	10
11	12	13	14	15	16	17
18	19	20	21	22	23	24
25	26	27	28	29	30	

JULY
M	T	W	T	F	S	S
						1
2	3	4	5	6	7	8
9	10	11	12	13	14	15
16	17	18	19	20	21	22
23	24	25	26	27	28	29
30	31					

AUGUST
M	T	W	T	F	S	S
		1	2	3	4	5
6	7	8	9	10	11	12
13	14	15	16	17	18	19
20	21	22	23	24	25	26
27	28	29	30	31		

SEPTEMBER
M	T	W	T	F	S	S
					1	2
3	4	5	6	7	8	9
10	11	12	13	14	15	16
17	18	19	20	21	22	23
24	25	26	27	28	29	30

OCTOBER
M	T	W	T	F	S	S
1	2	3	4	5	6	7
8	9	10	11	12	13	14
15	16	17	18	19	20	21
22	23	24	25	26	27	28
29	30	31				

NOVEMBER
M	T	W	T	F	S	S
			1	2	3	4
5	6	7	8	9	10	11
12	13	14	15	16	17	18
19	20	21	22	23	24	25
26	27	28	29	30		

DECEMBER
M	T	W	T	F	S	S
					1	2
3	4	5	6	7	8	9
10	11	12	13	14	15	16
17	18	19	20	21	22	23
24	25	26	27	28	29	30
31						

2019

JANUARY
M	T	W	T	F	S	S
	1	2	3	4	5	6
7	8	9	10	11	12	13
14	15	16	17	18	19	20
21	22	23	24	25	26	27
28	29	30	31			

FEBRUARY
M	T	W	T	F	S	S
				1	2	3
4	5	6	7	8	9	10
11	12	13	14	15	16	17
18	19	20	21	22	23	24
25	26	27	28			

MARCH
M	T	W	T	F	S	S
				1	2	3
4	5	6	7	8	9	10
11	12	13	14	15	16	17
18	19	20	21	22	23	24
25	26	27	28	29	30	31

APRIL
M	T	W	T	F	S	S
1	2	3	4	5	6	7
8	9	10	11	12	13	14
15	16	17	18	19	20	21
22	23	24	25	26	27	28
29	30					

MAY
M	T	W	T	F	S	S
		1	2	3	4	5
6	7	8	9	10	11	12
13	14	15	16	17	18	19
20	21	22	23	24	25	26
27	28	29	30	31		

JUNE
M	T	W	T	F	S	S
					1	2
3	4	5	6	7	8	9
10	11	12	13	14	15	16
17	18	19	20	21	22	23
24	25	26	27	28	29	30

JULY
M	T	W	T	F	S	S
1	2	3	4	5	6	7
8	9	10	11	12	13	14
15	16	17	18	19	20	21
22	23	24	25	26	27	28
29	30	31				

AUGUST
M	T	W	T	F	S	S
			1	2	3	4
5	6	7	8	9	10	11
12	13	14	15	16	17	18
19	20	21	22	23	24	25
26	27	28	29	30	31	

SEPTEMBER
M	T	W	T	F	S	S
						1
2	3	4	5	6	7	8
9	10	11	12	13	14	15
16	17	18	19	20	21	22
23	24	25	26	27	28	29
30						

OCTOBER
M	T	W	T	F	S	S
	1	2	3	4	5	6
7	8	9	10	11	12	13
14	15	16	17	18	19	20
21	22	23	24	25	26	27
28	29	30	31			

NOVEMBER
M	T	W	T	F	S	S
				1	2	3
4	5	6	7	8	9	10
11	12	13	14	15	16	17
18	19	20	21	22	23	24
25	26	27	28	29	30	

DECEMBER
M	T	W	T	F	S	S
						1
2	3	4	5	6	7	8
9	10	11	12	13	14	15
16	17	18	19	20	21	22
23	24	25	26	27	28	29
30	31					

2020

JANUARY
M	T	W	T	F	S	S
		1	2	3	4	5
6	7	8	9	10	11	12
13	14	15	16	17	18	19
20	21	22	23	24	25	26
27	28	29	30	31		

FEBRUARY
M	T	W	T	F	S	S
					1	2
3	4	5	6	7	8	9
10	11	12	13	14	15	16
17	18	19	20	21	22	23
24	25	26	27	28	29	

MARCH
M	T	W	T	F	S	S
						1
2	3	4	5	6	7	8
9	10	11	12	13	14	15
16	17	18	19	20	21	22
23	24	25	26	27	28	29
30	31					

APRIL
M	T	W	T	F	S	S
		1	2	3	4	5
6	7	8	9	10	11	12
13	14	15	16	17	18	19
20	21	22	23	24	25	26
27	28	29	30			

MAY
M	T	W	T	F	S	S
				1	2	3
4	5	6	7	8	9	10
11	12	13	14	15	16	17
18	19	20	21	22	23	24
25	26	27	28	29	30	31

JUNE
M	T	W	T	F	S	S
1	2	3	4	5	6	7
8	9	10	11	12	13	14
15	16	17	18	19	20	21
22	23	24	25	26	27	28
29	30					

JULY
M	T	W	T	F	S	S
		1	2	3	4	5
6	7	8	9	10	11	12
13	14	15	16	17	18	19
20	21	22	23	24	25	26
27	28	29	30	31		

AUGUST
M	T	W	T	F	S	S
					1	2
3	4	5	6	7	8	9
10	11	12	13	14	15	16
17	18	19	20	21	22	23
24	25	26	27	28	29	30
31						

SEPTEMBER
M	T	W	T	F	S	S
	1	2	3	4	5	6
7	8	9	10	11	12	13
14	15	16	17	18	19	20
21	22	23	24	25	26	27
28	29	30				

OCTOBER
M	T	W	T	F	S	S
			1	2	3	4
5	6	7	8	9	10	11
12	13	14	15	16	17	18
19	20	21	22	23	24	25
26	27	28	29	30	31	

NOVEMBER
M	T	W	T	F	S	S
						1
2	3	4	5	6	7	8
9	10	11	12	13	14	15
16	17	18	19	20	21	22
23	24	25	26	27	28	29
30						

DECEMBER
M	T	W	T	F	S	S
	1	2	3	4	5	6
7	8	9	10	11	12	13
14	15	16	17	18	19	20
21	22	23	24	25	26	27
28	29	30	31			

PERSONAL DETAILS

Name:

Address:

Phone: Mobile/Cell:

Email:

Important Numbers:

Passport No: Driving Licence No:

Travel Insurance No: Camera Serial No:

Others:

Medical Information:

Blood Group: Doctor:

Allergies/Medication:

Emergency Contact:

Other:

DECEMBER / JANUARY

Monday 31

Tuesday 1

New Year's Day
Republic Day (Slovakia)
Independence Day (Haiti)

Wednesday 2

Thursday 3

Friday 4

2018/2019

Saturday 5

Sunday 6

Epiphany

Life is either a daring adventure or nothing at all – Helen Keller

JANUARY

Monday 7

Tuesday 8

Orthodox Christmas Day

Wednesday 9

Thursday 10

Friday 11

2019

Saturday 12

Sunday 13

Rivers know this: there is no hurry. We shall get there some day – A.A.Milne

JANUARY

Monday 14

Tuesday 15

Wednesday 16

Thursday 17

Start of Sundance Film Festival (UT – USA)

Friday 18

2019

Saturday 19

Sunday 20

Not until we are lost do we begin to understand ourselves – Henry David Thoreau

JANUARY

Monday 21

Tu B'Shevat
Martin Luther King Day (USA)
Anniversary Day (Wellington – New Zealand)

Tuesday 22

Wednesday 23

Thursday 24

Friday 25

Robert Burns Night (Scotland)

2019

Saturday 26

Australia Day
Republic Day (India)

Sunday 27

Travel is fatal to prejudice, bigotry and narrow-mindedness – Mark Twain

JANUARY / FEBRUARY

Monday 28

Anniversary Day (Auckland – New Zealand)

Tuesday 29

Up Helly Aa Fire Festival (Shetland – Scotland)

Wednesday 30

Thursday 31

Friday 1

National Freedom Day (USA)

2019

Saturday 2

Groundhog Day (USA)

Sunday 3

One's destination is never a place, but a new way of seeing things – Henry Miller

SWITZERLAND

The birthplace of the skiing vacation was in Switzerland's Engadine Valley, 150 years ago. Resorts such as St Moritz are not cheap but in January there's nowhere better to barrel down a black run. There are also many miles of groomed trails for cross-country skiers. And in late December, the infamous Cresta toboggan track opens.

FEBRUARY

Monday 4

Independence Day (Sri Lanka)

Tuesday 5

Chinese New Year

Wednesday 6

Waitangi Day (New Zealand)

Thursday 7

Friday 8

Culture Day (Slovenia)

2019

Saturday 9

Sunday 10

Feast of St Paul's Shipwreck (Malta)

I haven't been everywhere but it's on my list – Susan Sontag

FEBRUARY

Monday 11

Tuesday 12

Wednesday 13

Thursday 14

St Valentine's Day
Start of Berlin Film Festival (Germany)

Friday 15

Statehood Day (Serbia)

Saturday 16

Independence Day (Lithuania)

Sunday 17

Two roads diverged in a wood and I – I took the one less travelled by,
and that has made all the difference – Robert Frost

FEBRUARY

Monday 18

Presidents' Day (USA)

Tuesday 19

Pingxi Sky Lantern Festival (Taiwan)

Wednesday 20

Thursday 21

Friday 22

Independence Day (St Lucia)

2019

Saturday 23

Start of Venice Carnival (Italy)

Sunday 24

Independence Day (Estonia)

Adventure is not outside man; it is within – George Eliot

FEBRUARY / MARCH

Monday 25

Tuesday 26

Wednesday 27

Independence Day (Dominican Republic)

Thursday 28

Friday 1

St David's Day (Wales)

2019

Saturday 2

Sunday 3

Liberation Day (Bulgaria)
Carnaval Sunday (Rio de Janeiro – Brazil)

*Travelling... it leaves you speechless,
then turns you into a storyteller* – Ibn Battuta

MARCH

Monday 4

Tuesday 5

Shrove Tuesday
New Orleans Mardi Gras (LA – USA)

Wednesday 6

Ash Wednesday
Independence Day (Ghana)

Thursday 7

Friday 8

Saturday 9

Sunday 10

Start of Daylight Saving Time (Canada, USA)

*Don't tell me how educated you are, tell me
how much you travelled – Mohammed*

MARCH

Monday 11

Adelaide Cup (SA – Australia)/Canberra Day (ACT – Australia)/
Eight Hours Day (TAS – Australia)/Labour Day (VIC – Australia)
Independence Restoration Day (Lithuania)

Tuesday 12

Wednesday 13

Thursday 14

Friday 15

Revolution Day (Hungary)

2019

Saturday 16

Sunday 17

St Patrick's Day

There are only two emotions in a plane: boredom and terror – Orson Welles

MARCH

Monday 18

Tuesday 19

Feast of St Joseph (Malta)

Wednesday 20

March Equinox
Start of Holi Festival (India, Nepal)
Independence Day (Tunisia)

Thursday 21

Purim
Human Rights Day (South Africa)

Friday 22

Pakistan Day

2019

Saturday 23

Sunday 24

*Like all great travellers, I have seen more than I remember,
and remember more than I have seen* – Benjamin Disraeli

ICELAND

February in Iceland is not as cold as you might expect: the Gulf Stream keeps this island warmer than New York City on average. Wintry activities include glacier hikes, snowmobile safaris and superjeep drives across volcanoes. Look to the night skies for displays of the Northern Lights.

SICILY, ITALY

In early spring, the Mediterranean's largest island opens its doors as the days lengthen. Explore such historic sites as the Greek theatre of Siracusa and temples at Agrigento, the medieval cathedral at Monreale and numerous baroque towns. Prices are lower and there will be fewer tourists.

© Matt Munro

MARCH

Monday 25

Independence Day (Cyprus, Greece)

Tuesday 26

Independence Day (Bangladesh)

Wednesday 27

Thursday 28

Friday 29

2019

Saturday 30

Sunday 31

Mothering Sunday (Ireland, UK)
Start of Daylight Saving Time (Ireland, UK)
Freedom Day (Malta)

I never travel without my diary. One should always have
something sensational to read in the train – Oscar Wilde

APRIL

Monday 1

Greek Cypriot Day (Cyprus)

Tuesday 2

Wednesday 3

Isra and Mi'raj

Thursday 4

Independence Day (Senegal)

Friday 5

2019

Saturday 6

Sunday 7

End of Daylight Saving Time (Australia, New Zealand)

One way to get the most out of life is to look upon it as an adventure – William Feather

APRIL

Monday 8

Tuesday 9

Wednesday 10

Thursday 11

Friday 12

2019

Saturday 13

Start of Songkran Water Festival (Thailand)

Sunday 14

*All travel has its advantages. If the passenger visits better countries, he may learn to improve his own.
And if fortune carries him to worse, he may learn to enjoy it – Samuel Johnson*

APRIL

Monday 15

Tuesday 16

Wednesday 17

Thursday 18

Maundy Thursday

Friday 19

Good Friday

2019

Saturday 20

Start of Passover

Sunday 21

Easter Sunday

*When you travel, remember that a foreign country is not designed to make you comfortable.
It is designed to make its own people comfortable – Clifton Fadiman*

APRIL

Monday 22

Tuesday 23

St George's Day (England)

Wednesday 24

Thursday 25

Liberation Day (Italy, Portugal)
ANZAC Day (Australia, New Zealand)

Friday 26

End of Passover

2019

Saturday 27

Resistance Day (Slovenia)
Freedom Day (South Africa)
King's Birthday (Netherlands)

Sunday 28

Every exit is an entry somewhere else – Tom Stoppard

APRIL / MAY

Monday 29

Tuesday 30

Wednesday 1

May Day
Yom HaShoah

Thursday 2

Friday 3

Constitution Day (Poland)

Saturday 4

Restoration of Independence Day (Latvia)

Sunday 5

Cinco de Mayo

Not all those who wander are lost – J.R.R. Tolkien

MAY

Monday 6

Tuesday 7

Wednesday 8

Thursday 9

Friday 10

2019

Saturday 11

Sunday 12

Mother's Day (Australia, Canada, New Zealand, USA)

I dislike feeling at home when I am abroad – George Bernard Shaw

CALIFORNIA
USA

The Pacific Ocean and the American coast come to their most sensational blows at Big Sur, between Carmel-by-the-Sea and San Simeon. April is a great month to drive Hwy 1, with clear skies, warm temperatures and less traffic than summer. Take your time and dally on the headlands and beaches.

MOROCCO

Morocco is marvellous in May. The Valley of the Roses at the foot of the High Atlas Mountains is particularly pretty during its mid-May flower festival. The green valleys of the Atlas range are good for hiking, although the nights remain chilly.

© Lottie Davies

MAY

Monday 13

Tuesday 14

Wednesday 15

Thursday 16

Friday 17

Constitution Day (Norway)

Saturday 18

Sunday 19

It is better to travel well than to arrive – Buddha

MAY

Monday 20

Victoria Day (Canada)

Tuesday 21

Wednesday 22

Thursday 23

Friday 24

Culture & Literacy Day (Bulgaria)

2019

Saturday 25

Revolution Day (Argentina)
Independence Day (Jordan)

Sunday 26

Independence Day (Georgia)

All journeys have secret destinations of which the traveller is unaware – Martin Buber

MAY / JUNE

Monday 27

Memorial Day (USA)
Spring Bank Holiday (UK)

Tuesday 28

Wednesday 29

Thursday 30

Start of Cricket World Cup (England & Wales)

Friday 31

2019

Saturday 1

UEFA Champions League Final (Madrid, Spain)

Sunday 2

Republic Day (Italy)

Travel brings power and love back into your life – Rumi

JUNE

Monday 3

Tuesday 4

Wednesday 5

Thursday 6

Friday 7

2019

Saturday 8

Sunday 9

We live in a wonderful world that is full of beauty, charm and adventure. There is no end to the adventures we can have if only we seek them with our eyes open – Jawaharlal Nehru

JUNE

Monday 10

Portugal Day

Tuesday 11

Wednesday 12

Russia Day
Independence Day (Philippines)

Thursday 13

Friday 14

Saturday 15

Sunday 16

Youth Day (South Africa)
Father's Day (Canada, UK, USA)

A good traveller has no fixed plans and is not intent on arriving – **Lao Tzu**

JUNE

Monday 17

Icelandic National Day

Tuesday 18

Wednesday 19

Thursday 20

Friday 21

June Solstice

2019

Saturday 22

Sunday 23

Victory Day (Estonia)
Midsummer Eve (Latvia)

There are no foreign lands. It is the traveller only who is foreign
– Robert Louis Stevenson

JUNE

Monday 24

St John's Day (Estonia, Latvia, Lithuania)

Tuesday 25

Statehood Day (Slovenia)
Independence Day (Mozambique)

Wednesday 26

Independence Day (Madagascar)

Thursday 27

Friday 28

2019

Saturday 29

Sunday 30

A journey is like marriage. The certain way to be wrong
is to think you control it – John Steinbeck

BALI
INDONESIA

Visit Indonesia's twin tropical paradises, the islands of Bali and Lombok, in June before the school holidays. The weather is dry and warm, perfect for visiting Hindu temples, climbing volcanoes, surfing Bali's west coast breaks, snorkelling or simply getting horizontal on the sand.

© Pete Seaward

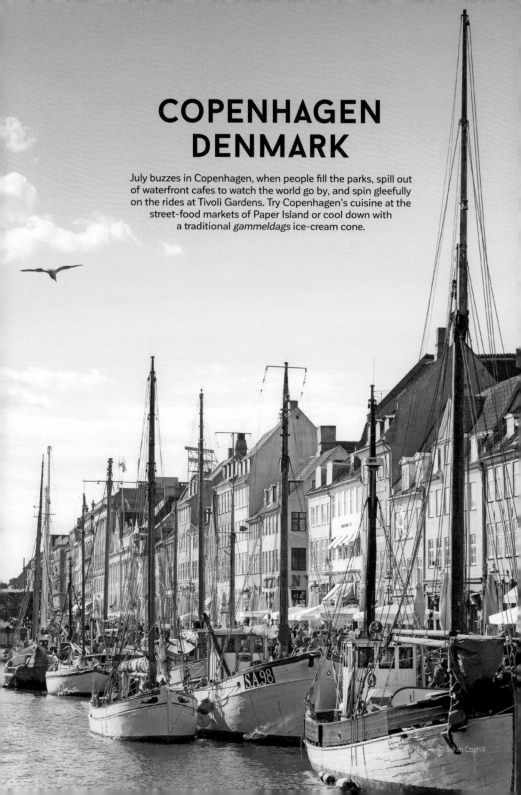

COPENHAGEN DENMARK

July buzzes in Copenhagen, when people fill the parks, spill out of waterfront cafes to watch the world go by, and spin gleefully on the rides at Tivoli Gardens. Try Copenhagen's cuisine at the street-food markets of Paper Island or cool down with a traditional *gammeldags* ice-cream cone.

JULY

Monday 1

Canada Day

Tuesday 2

Wednesday 3

Thursday 4

Independence Day (USA)

Friday 5

St Cyril and St Methodius Day (Czech Republic, Slovakia)

2019

Saturday 6

Jan Hus Day (Czech Republic)
King Mindaugas' Day (Lithuania)
Start of San Firmin Festival (Pamplona – Spain)

Sunday 7

It is not down in any map; true places
never are – Herman Melville

JULY

Monday 8

Tuesday 9

Wednesday 10

Thursday 11

Friday 12

2019

Saturday 13

National Day (Montenegro)

Sunday 14

Bastille Day (France)

*We wander for distraction, but we travel
for fulfilment* – Hilare Belloc

JULY

Monday 15

Cricket World Cup Final (England)

Tuesday 16

Wednesday 17

Thursday 18

Friday 19

2019

Saturday 20

Independence Day (Colombia)

Sunday 21

National Day (Belgium)

People don't take trips... trips take people
– John Steinbeck

JULY

Monday 22

Tuesday 23

Revolution Day (Egypt)

Wednesday 24

Thursday 25

Friday 26

Start of Tomorrowland Music Festival (Boom – Belgium)

2019

Saturday 27

Sunday 28

Fiestas Patrias (Peru)

Bizarre travel plans are dancing lessons from God – Kurt Vonnegut

JULY / AUGUST

Monday 29

Tuesday 30

Wednesday 31

Thursday 1

Friday 2

Start of Edinburgh Festival (Scotland)

2019

Saturday 3

Sunday 4

Certainly, travel is more than the seeing of sights; it is a change that goes on, deep and permanent, in the ideas of living – Mary Ritter Beard

AUGUST

Monday 5

Tuesday 6

Wednesday 7

Thursday 8

Friday 9

2019

Saturday 10

Independence Day (Ecuador)

Sunday 11

The journey not the arrival matters – T.S. Eliot

AUGUST

Monday 12

Eid-al-Adha

Tuesday 13

Wednesday 14

Thursday 15

Friday 16

2019

Saturday 17

Independence Day (Indonesia)

Sunday 18

The world is a book and those who do not travel read only one page – St Augustine

PAPUA NEW GUINEA

Explore this rugged land in August when rain is at its lowest ebb and Papua's two major 'sing-sings' are held: the Sepik River Crocodile Festival in Ambunti and the famed Mt Hagen Cultural Show. Both gather dozens of tribes for a bonanza of music and dance. It's also a good time to tackle the Kokoda Track.

SOUTH AFRICA

Visit South Africa in September and it seems as if the whole country has put on a show: the west is festooned with wildflowers; southern right whales gather off Cape Agulhas, southeast of Cape Town; big swells keep rolling in to thrill surfers along the Wild Coast; and wildlife gathers around waterholes in reserves.

© Lottie Davies

AUGUST

Monday 19

Tuesday 20

National Day (Hungary)
Independence Restoration Day (Estonia)

Wednesday 21

Thursday 22

Friday 23

2019

Saturday 24

Independence Day (Ukraine)

Sunday 25

Independence Day (Uruguay)

Wherever you go, go with all your heart – Confucius

AUGUST / SEPTEMBER

Monday 26

August Bank Holiday (England, Wales, Northern Ireland)

Tuesday 27

Wednesday 28

La Tomatina Festival (Spain)

Thursday 29

Slovak National Uprising Day (Slovakia)

Friday 30

2019

Saturday 31

Al-Hijra

Sunday 1

Constitution Day (Slovakia)
Father's Day (Australia, New Zealand)

I travel not to go anywhere, but to go. I travel for travel's sake.
The great affair is to move – Robert Louis Stevenson

SEPTEMBER

Monday 2

Labour Day (Canada, USA)
Independence Day (Vietnam)

Tuesday 3

Wednesday 4

Thursday 5

Friday 6

Unification Day (Bulgaria)
Start of Cascamorras (Granada – Spain)

2019

Saturday 7

Independence Day (Brazil)

Sunday 8

Feast of Our Lady of Victories (Malta)

*It is good to have an end to journey toward; but it is the
journey that matters, in the end – Ursula K Le Guin*

SEPTEMBER

Monday 9

Tuesday 10

Ashura

Wednesday 11

Thursday 12

Ethiopian New Year

Friday 13

2019

Saturday 14

Sunday 15

Day of Our Lady of Sorrows (Slovakia)

I have found out that there ain't no surer way to find out whether you like people or hate them than to travel with them – Mark Twain

SEPTEMBER

Monday 16

Independence Day (Mexico)

Tuesday 17

Wednesday 18

Independence Day (Chile)

Thursday 19

Friday 20

Start of Rugby World Cup (Japan)

2019

Saturday 21

Independence Day (Malta)
Start of Oktoberfest (Munich – Germany)

Sunday 22

Independence Day (Bulgaria)

Travel makes one modest, you see what a tiny place you occupy in the world
– Gustave Flaubert

SEPTEMBER

Monday 23

September Equinox

Tuesday 24

Heritage Day (South Africa)

Wednesday 25

Thursday 26

Friday 27

Meskel (Ethiopia)

2019

Saturday 28

Start of Athletics World Championships (Qatar)
Czech Statehood Day (Czech Republic)

Sunday 29

Start of Daylight Saving Time (New Zealand)

Make voyages! Attempt them... there's nothing else – Tennessee Williams

SEPTEMBER / OCTOBER

Monday 30

Rosh Hashanah
Family & Community Day (ACT – Australia)

Tuesday 1

National Day (China)
Independence Day (Cyprus, Nigeria)

Wednesday 2

Thursday 3

Unity Day (Germany)

Friday 4

2019

Saturday 5

Sunday 6

Start of Daylight Saving Time (Australia)

Travel is glamorous only in retrospect – Paul Theroux

THE DOURO PORTUGAL

Float down the Douro River in autumn, when the sun is still warm and the grape-heavy vines turn golden. You'll cruise past tiny towns plastered with azulejo tiles and numerous *quintas* (wineries) where you can stop for tastings. This region, now listed by Unesco, is where the provenance of wine was first authenticated.

BARBADOS

Storms should have died down but peak season hasn't started in November on Barbados. There's a beach for everyone, glamorous hotels, cliff-top yoga retreats, family-run guesthouses and late-night fish-frys. And lots of rum. Take a cultural detour in the Garrison area of the capital Bridgetown.

OCTOBER

Monday 7

Labour Day (ACT, NSW, SA – Australia)

Tuesday 8

Independence Day (Croatia)

Wednesday 9

Yom Kippur

Thursday 10

Friday 11

2019

Saturday 12

Hispanic Day (Spain)

Sunday 13

Adventure is worthwhile in itself – Amelia Earhart

OCTOBER

Monday 14

Start of Sukkot
Thanksgiving Day (Canada)
Columbus Day (USA)

Tuesday 15

Wednesday 16

Thursday 17

Friday 18

2019

Saturday 19

Sunday 20

For the born traveller, travelling is a besetting vice. Like other vices, it is imperious, demanding its victim's time, money, energy and the sacrifice of comfort – Aldous Huxley

OCTOBER

Monday 21

Tuesday 22

Wednesday 23

Republic Day (Hungary)

Thursday 24

Independence Day (Zambia)

Friday 25

2019

Saturday 26

Sunday 27

The real voyage of discovery consists not in seeking new landscapes,
but in having new eyes – Marcel Proust

OCTOBER / NOVEMBER

Monday 28

Labour Day (New Zealand)
October Holiday (Ireland)
Independent Czechoslovak State Day (Czech Republic)

Tuesday 29

Republic Day (Turkey)

Wednesday 30

Thursday 31

Halloween
Reformation Day (Slovenia)

Friday 1

All Saints Day
Revolution Day (Algeria)
Remembrance Day (Slovenia)

Saturday 2

Day of the Dead (Mexico)
Rugby World Cup Final (Japan)

Sunday 3

*The first condition of understanding a foreign
country is to smell it* – Rudyard Kipling

NOVEMBER

Monday 4

Tuesday 5

Guy Fawkes Night (England)

Wednesday 6

Thursday 7

Friday 8

2019

Saturday 9

Independence Day (Cambodia)

Sunday 10

Remembrance Sunday (UK)

A ship is safe in harbour, but that is not what ships are for – William G.T. Shedd

NOVEMBER

Monday 11

Veterans Day (USA)
Remembrance Day (Commonwealth)

Tuesday 12

Wednesday 13

Thursday 14

Friday 15

2019

Saturday 16

Sunday 17

Struggle for Freedom & Democracy Day (Czech Republic, Slovakia)

To awaken quite alone in a strange town is one of the
pleasantest sensations in the world – Freya Stark

NOVEMBER

Monday 18

Proclamation of the Republic (Latvia)

Tuesday 19

Wednesday 20

Thursday 21

Friday 22

2019

Saturday 23

Sunday 24

*The use of traveling is to regulate imagination by reality, and instead of thinking
how things may be, to see them as they are* – Samuel Johnson

SAN SEBASTIÁN SPAIN

Savour San Sebastián's *pintxos* bars and abundant starred restaurants in mild December, when low tourist numbers mean great value accommodation and less competition for tables. Work up an appetite with a bracing walk along Playa de la Concha or up Monte Igueldo for views across this beautiful city on the bay.

© Justin Foulkes

NOVEMBER / DECEMBER

Monday 25

National Day (Bosnia and Herzegovina)

Tuesday 26

Wednesday 27

Thursday 28

Thanksgiving Day (USA)
Independence Day (Albania)

Friday 29

2019

Saturday 30

St Andrew's Day (Scotland)

Sunday 1

National Day (Romania)
Independence Restoration Day (Portugal)

Perhaps travel cannot prevent bigotry, but by demonstrating that all peoples cry, laugh, eat, worry and die, it can introduce the idea that if we try and understand each other, we may even become friends – Maya Angelou

DECEMBER

Monday 2

National Day (UAE)
National Day (Laos)

Tuesday 3

Wednesday 4

Thursday 5

Friday 6

Constitution Day (Spain)
Independence Day (Finland)

2019

Saturday 7

Sunday 8

We shall not cease from our exploring and the end of all our exploring will be to arrive where we started and know the place for the first time – T.S. Eliot

DECEMBER

Monday 9

Tuesday 10

Wednesday 11

Thursday 12

Jamhuri Day (Kenya)

Friday 13

Republic Day (Malta)

2019

Saturday 14

Sunday 15

Never go on trips with anyone you do not love – Ernest Hemingway

DECEMBER

Monday 16

Independence Day (Kazakhstan)
Day of Reconciliation (South Africa)

Tuesday 17

Wednesday 18

Thursday 19

Friday 20

2019

Saturday 21

Sunday 22

Winter Solstice
Start of Hanukkah

*One of the great things about travel is that you find out how
many good, kind people there are – Edith Wharton*

DECEMBER

Monday 23

Tuesday 24

Christmas Eve

Wednesday 25

Christmas Day

Thursday 26

Boxing Day / St Stephen's Day
Day of Goodwill (South Africa)

Friday 27

2019

Saturday 28

Sunday 29

I may not have gone where I intended to go, but I think I have
ended up where I intended to be – Douglas Adams

DECEMBER / JANUARY

Monday 30

Tuesday 31

New Year's Eve

Wednesday 1

New Year's Day

Thursday 2

Friday 3

2019 / 2020

Saturday 4

Sunday 5

Paris is always a good idea – Audrey Heburn

Published by Lonely Planet Global Limited
CRN 554153
www.lonelyplanet.com
ISBN 978 17870 1730 6
© Lonely Planet 2017
© Photographs as indicated 2017
Printed in Malaysia

Managing Director, Publishing Piers Pickard
Associate Publisher & Commissioning Editor Robin Barton
Editor Nick Mee
Print Production Larissa Frost, Nigel Longuet

STAY IN TOUCH lonelyplanet.com/contact

AUSTRALIA The Malt Store, Level 3, 551 Swanston St,
Carlton, Victoria 3053 T: 03 8379 8000

IRELAND Unit E, Digital Court, The Digital Hub,
Rainsford St, Dublin 8

USA 124 Linden St, Oakland, CA 94607
T: 510 250 6400

UK 240 Blackfriars Rd, London SE1 8NW
T: 020 3771 5100